LEARNING FRACTIONS

USING
LEGO® BRICKS
STUDENT EDITION

Dr. Shirley Disseler

COMPASS

Learning Fractions Using LEGO® Bricks — Student Edition

Copyright ©2016 by Shirley Disseler
Published by Brigantine Media/Compass Publishing
211 North Avenue, St. Johnsbury, Vermont 05819

Cover and book design by Anne LoCascio
Illustrations by Curt Spannraft

Brigantine Media/Compass Publishing
211 North Avenue
St. Johnsbury, Vermont 05819
Phone: 802-751-8802
Fax: 802-751-8804
E-mail: neil@brigantinemedia.com
Website: www.compasspublishing.org

ORDERING INFORMATION
Quantity sales
Special discounts for schools are available for quantity purchases of physical books and digital downloads.
For information, contact Brigantine Media at the address shown above or visit
www.compasspublishing.org.

Individual sales
Brigantine Media/Compass Publishing publications are available through most booksellers.
They can also be ordered directly from the publisher.
Phone: 802-751-8802 | Fax: 802-751-8804
www.compasspublishing.org
ISBN 978-1-9384065-8-4

CONTENTS

PARTS OF A FRACTION

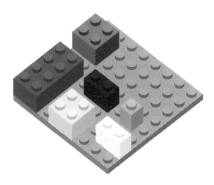

Models of 1/2

1. Use LEGO® bricks to model ½ in two more ways. Draw your models. Circle the numerators in red and the denominators in black.

2. Use LEGO® bricks to model ¼. Draw your model. Circle the numerator in red and the denominator in black.

How do you know your model shows ¼?

_____

_____

_____

Which is larger, ¼ or ½? How do you know?

_____

_____

_____

3. Use LEGO® bricks to model ⅛. Draw your model. Circle the numerator in red and the denominator in black.

How do you know it is ⅛?

_____

_____

_____

Challenge Problem: Model ⅜. Draw your model. Circle the numerator in red and the denominator in black.

Assessment:

1. Explain what the word *numerator* means.

_____

_____

_____

2. Explain what the word *denominator* means.

_____

_____

_____

3. Circle all the numerators in these fractions:

$\dfrac{2}{4}$ $\dfrac{5}{6}$ $\dfrac{7}{8}$ $\dfrac{6}{9}$

4. Circle all the denominators in these fractions:

$\dfrac{3}{7}$ $\dfrac{8}{9}$ $\dfrac{4}{5}$ $\dfrac{2}{7}$

5. Using LEGO® bricks, show which is larger, $\frac{1}{4}$ or $\frac{3}{8}$. Draw your model.

BENCHMARK FRACTIONS

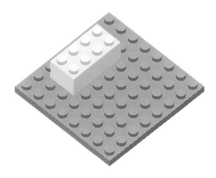

1. This shows a 2x4 brick as the whole. How many studs are there? _____

What do the studs represent?

_____

_____

_____

2. If the 2x4 brick is the whole, use LEGO® bricks to show ½ of that whole. Draw your model.

3. Use bricks to show ¼ of that same whole (the 2x4 brick). Draw your model.

4. Use bricks to show ⅛ of that same whole (the 2x4 brick). Draw your model.

5. Use bricks to show ¾ of that same whole (the 2x4 brick). Draw your model.

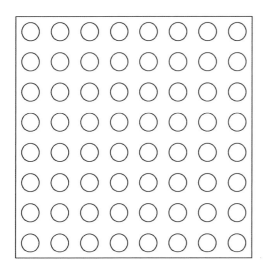

6. Place one 2x4 brick on a base plate. Place one 2x3 brick next to it.

Which brick needs to be added to the 2x3 brick to make the model the same length as the whole? _____ Draw your model.

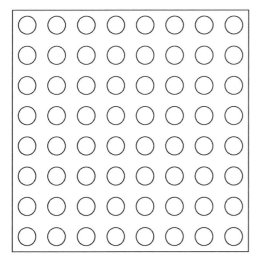

More problems for practice:

7. Place a 1x6 brick on a base plate. Use a brick to show ½ of this whole.
Which brick? _____ Draw your model.

8. Place a 1x6 brick on a base plate. Use a brick to show ⅓ of this whole.
Which brick? _____ Draw your model.

Explain your thinking.

_____

_____

_____

9. Place a 1x6 brick on a base plate. Use a brick to show ¹⁄₆ of this whole.
Which brick? _____ Draw your model.

Explain your thinking.

_____

_____

_____

Assessment:

Why is ¹⁄₂ of the 2x4 brick larger than ¹⁄₂ of the 2x3 brick? Prove your answer with a model and draw it.

Explain your thinking.

_____

_____

_____

ADDING FRACTIONS WITH LIKE DENOMINATORS

1. With bricks, model $\frac{1}{6}$ + $\frac{2}{6}$ and the solution. Draw your model.

2. With bricks, make a model to show that $\frac{3}{6}$ = $\frac{1}{2}$. Draw your model.

How do you know it is ½?

_____

_____

_____

3. With bricks, model ⁶/₁₄ + ⁴/₁₄ + ²/₁₄ = _____ . Draw your model.

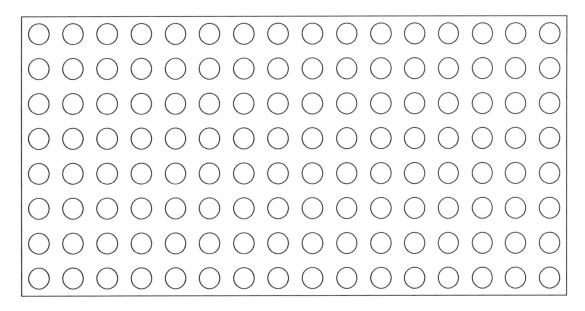

With bricks, model the solution. Draw your model.

Explain your thinking.

_____

_____

_____

More problems for practice:

4. With bricks, model $\frac{4}{6} + \frac{2}{6} =$ _____. Draw your model.

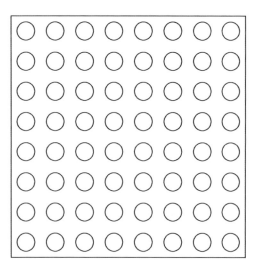

With bricks, model the solution. Draw your model.

What do you notice? Explain your thinking.

_____

_____

_____

5. With bricks, make a model to show $^2/_4 + {}^3/_4 =$ _____. Draw your model.

With bricks, model the solution. Draw your model.

What do you notice? Explain your thinking.

_____

_____

_____

Assessment:

1. With bricks, add $\frac{3}{6} + \frac{2}{6}$. Draw your model and the solution.

Explain your thinking.

_____

_____

_____

2. With bricks, add $\frac{1}{8} + \frac{3}{8}$. Draw your model and the solution.

Explain your thinking.

_____

_____

_____

SUBTRACTING FRACTIONS WITH LIKE DENOMINATORS

1. With bricks, model $^4/_{12} - {^1/_{12}}$. Draw your model.

Circle the fraction that is the minuend: $^4/_{12}$ $^1/_{12}$

Why is that fraction the minuend?

_____

_____

_____

With bricks, model the solution to $^4/_{12}$ - $^1/_{12}$. Draw your model.

Challenge: With bricks, show the solution in simplest form. Draw your model.

Explain your thinking.

_____

_____

_____

More problems for practice:

2. With bricks, model $\frac{4}{6} - \frac{1}{6}$. Draw your model.

With bricks, model the solution. Draw your model.

With bricks, show the solution in the simplest form. Draw your model.

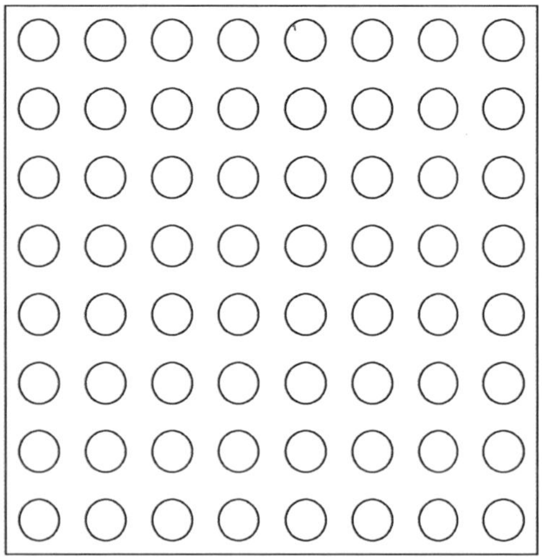

Explain your thinking.

_____

_____

_____

3. With bricks, model $6/8 - 2/8$. Draw your model.

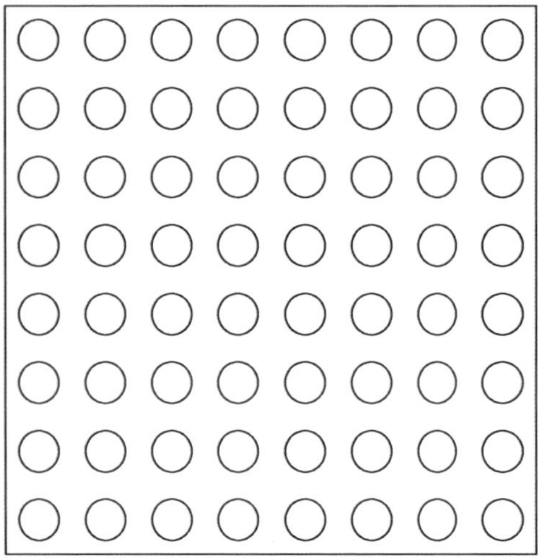

With bricks, show the solution. Draw your model.

What do you notice? Explain your thinking.

_____

_____

_____

With bricks, show the solution in simplest form. Draw your model.

Assessment:

1. With bricks, subtract ³/₆ - ²/₆. Draw your model and the solution.

[grid of circles]

Explain your thinking.

_____

_____

_____

2. With bricks, subtract ⁴/₈ - ²/₈. Draw your model and the solution.

[grid of circles]

Explain your thinking.

_____

_____

_____

Show the solution in simplest form.

3. With bricks, subtract $^{6}/_{12} - ^{4}/_{12}$. Draw your model and the solution.

Explain your thinking.

_____

_____

_____

5

FACTORS

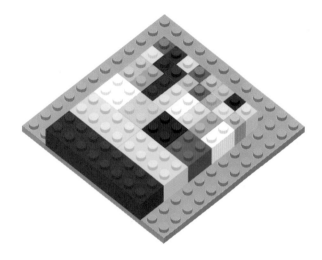

1. Build this model with bricks to show all the factors of 16:

Step 1: Place a 2x8 brick on a base plate.

Step 2: Find two bricks of equal size that together are equivalent in size to the 16-stud brick and show two halves of the 16-stud brick. Place them next to the 16-stud brick.

Step 3: Find four bricks of equal size equivalent in size to the 16-stud brick and place them next to the step 2 bricks.

Step 4: Find the next number of equal-sized bricks that are equivalent to the size of the 16-stud brick and place them next to the step 3 bricks.

Step 5: Find the next number of equal-sized bricks that are equivalent to the size of the 16-stud brick and place them next to the step 4 bricks.

Draw your model.

Using the model, list all the factors of 16.

_____

_____

_____

2. Make a model with bricks to show all the factors of 6. Follow the same steps by finding all the bricks that together are equivalent in size to a 6-stud brick.

Draw your model.

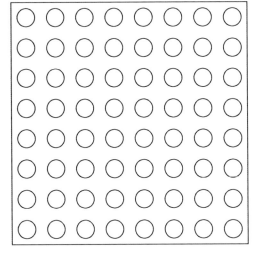

Using the model, list all the factors of 6.

_____

_____

_____

3. Make a model with bricks to show all the factors of 8. Follow the same steps by finding all the bricks that together are equivalent in size to an 8-stud brick.

Draw your model.

```
○ ○ ○ ○ ○ ○ ○ ○
○ ○ ○ ○ ○ ○ ○ ○
○ ○ ○ ○ ○ ○ ○ ○
○ ○ ○ ○ ○ ○ ○ ○
○ ○ ○ ○ ○ ○ ○ ○
○ ○ ○ ○ ○ ○ ○ ○
○ ○ ○ ○ ○ ○ ○ ○
○ ○ ○ ○ ○ ○ ○ ○
```

Using the model, list all the factors of 8.

_____

_____

_____

More problems for practice:

4. Make a model with bricks to show all the factors of 12. Draw your model and explain your thinking.

_____

_____

_____

5. Make a model with bricks to show all the factors of 4. Draw your model and explain your thinking.

_____

_____

_____

Assessment:

1. Which of the following is not a factor of 8? How do you know?

   3   4   2   1

Prove your answer using a brick model. Draw your model and explain your thinking.

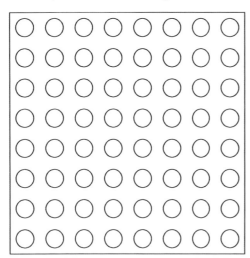

_____

_____

2. Choose another number and make a model with bricks to show all the factors of that number. Draw your model and explain your thinking.

_____

_____

EQUIVALENT FRACTIONS

1. Build this 16ths model. Draw your model and label the fractions.

Use the model to answer the following questions:

a. How many eighths are in the 16ths model? _____

b. How many fourths are in the 16ths model? _____

c. How many one-stud bricks are in the 16ths model? _____

2. With bricks, build a model that shows twelfths. Draw your model. Label the whole, all the halves, the thirds, the fourths, the sixths, and the twelfths. Explain how many bricks make up each of these fractional parts of the whole.

_____

_____

_____

More problems for practice:

3. Build a model that shows 24ths. Label all of the equivalent fractional parts of this whole. Draw your model and list the number of bricks in the equivalent parts of the model.

_____

_____

_____

4. Build a model that shows 18ths. Label all of the equivalent fractional parts of this whole. Draw your model and list the number of bricks in the equivalent parts of the model.

_____

_____

_____

Assessment:

1. Build a model for 8ths. Show all the equivalent fractions for 8. Draw your model and explain its parts.

_____

_____

_____

2. Prove that $^3/_6 = {}^1/_2$ using what you learned in this lesson. Draw your solution and explain.

_____

_____

_____

3. Write a definition of *equivalent fractions* based on what you learned in this lesson.

_____

_____

_____

ADDING FRACTIONS WITH UNLIKE DENOMINATORS

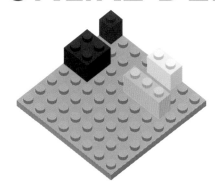

1. This model shows ¼ + ⅔. Build this model with bricks.

Draw your model and label the fractions.

Add bricks to each denominator until they both show an equal number of studs. How many studs are there in each denominator? _____
How many bricks did you add to the ¼ fraction? _____
How many bricks did you add to the ⅔ fraction? _____

Find the numerator of the ¼ fraction. Add the same number of bricks to the numerator that were added to the denominator. How many bricks did you add?_____

Find the numerator of the ⅔ fraction. Add the same number of bricks to the numerator that were added to the denominator. How many bricks did you add? _____

With the denominators the same, add the total number of studs in both numerators. How many studs are in the total numerator? _____ How many studs are in the denominator? _____

Write the equation for the fraction addition problem: _____

Draw your solution.

2. With bricks, model the steps for adding $\frac{1}{2} + \frac{3}{4}$. Draw your model on the left base plate and label the fractions.

With bricks, model the steps to find the solution. Draw your model on the right base plate and explain your thinking. What do you notice that is different with this solution?

_____

_____

_____

Challenge: Can you model the mixed number? How do you know it is a mixed number?

_____

_____

_____

More problems for practice:

3. With bricks, build a model $\frac{2}{3} + \frac{3}{4}$. Draw your model and label the fractions.

With bricks, model the steps to find the solution. Draw your model and explain your thinking.

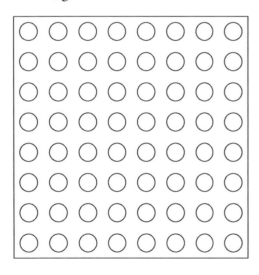

_____

_____

_____

Identify the mixed number and draw the model. Circle and label the part of the model that shows the whole number in the mixed fraction.

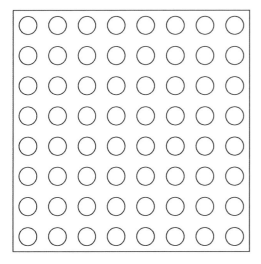

Assessment:

1. With bricks, model $\frac{1}{2} + \frac{4}{8}$. Draw your model and explain your solution.

_____
_____
_____

2. With bricks, model ³⁄₆ + ²⁄₃. Draw your model and explain your solution.

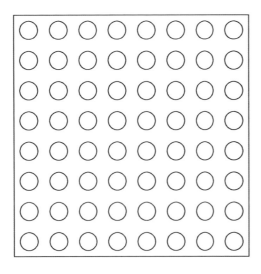 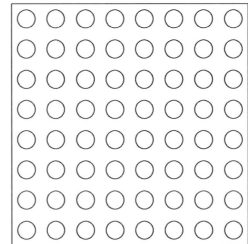

_____

_____

_____

3. What is a mixed fraction? How do you know if you have one?

_____

_____

_____

SUBTRACTING FRACTIONS WITH UNLIKE DENOMINATORS

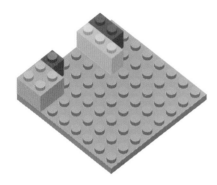

1. This model shows ²/₃ - ¹/₄. Build this model with bricks.

Draw your model and label the fractions.

○ ○ ○ ○ ○ ○ ○ ○
○ ○ ○ ○ ○ ○ ○ ○
○ ○ ○ ○ ○ ○ ○ ○
○ ○ ○ ○ ○ ○ ○ ○
○ ○ ○ ○ ○ ○ ○ ○
○ ○ ○ ○ ○ ○ ○ ○
○ ○ ○ ○ ○ ○ ○ ○
○ ○ ○ ○ ○ ○ ○ ○

Add bricks to each denominator until they both show an equal number of studs. How many studs are there in each denominator? _____

How many bricks did you add to the ²/₃ fraction? _____

How many bricks did you add to the ¹/₄ fraction? _____

Find the numerator of the ²/₃ fraction. Add the same number of bricks to the numerator that were added to the denominator. How many bricks did you add? _____

Find the numerator of the ¹/₄ fraction. Add the same number of bricks to the numerator that were added to the denominator. How many bricks did you add? _____

Stack the studs from the numerator of the ¹/₄ fraction on top of the numerator of the ²/₃ fraction. Count the number of bricks in the numerator that are uncovered. How many are uncovered? _____ This number represents the numerator for the solution fraction.

How many studs are in the denominator? _____. This number represents the denominator for the solution fraction.

Write the equation for the fraction subtraction problem: _____

Draw your solution.

| ○ ○ ○ ○ ○ ○ ○ ○ |
| ○ ○ ○ ○ ○ ○ ○ ○ |
| ○ ○ ○ ○ ○ ○ ○ ○ |
| ○ ○ ○ ○ ○ ○ ○ ○ |
| ○ ○ ○ ○ ○ ○ ○ ○ |
| ○ ○ ○ ○ ○ ○ ○ ○ |
| ○ ○ ○ ○ ○ ○ ○ ○ |
| ○ ○ ○ ○ ○ ○ ○ ○ |

2. With bricks, model the steps for subtracting $3/4 - 1/2$. Draw your model and label the fractions.

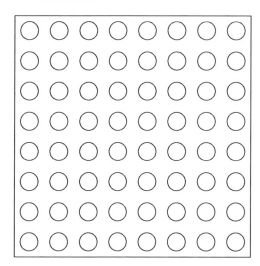

With bricks, model the steps to find the solution. Draw your model and explain your thinking.

_____

_____

_____

More problems for practice:

3. With bricks, model $3/4 - 2/3$. Draw your model on the left diagram and label the fractions.

With bricks, model the steps to find the solution. Draw your model on the right diagram and explain your thinking.

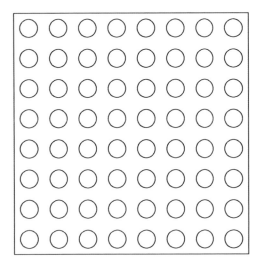

_____

_____

4. With bricks, model $6/8 - 1/4$. Draw your model on the left diagram and label the fractions.

With bricks, model the steps to find the solution. Draw your model on the right diagram and explain your thinking.

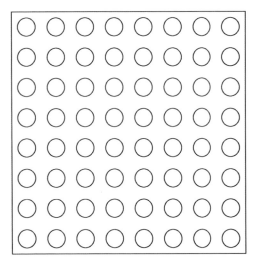

_____

_____

5. With bricks, model $^4/_8$ - $^2/_4$. Draw your model on the left diagram and label the fractions.

With bricks, model the steps to find the solution. Draw your model on the right diagram and explain your thinking. What is different about this problem?

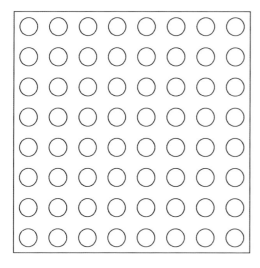 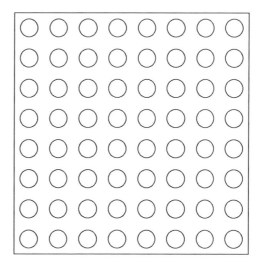

_____

_____

_____

Assessment:

1. With bricks, model $^1/_2$ + $^2/_8$. Draw your model, label the fractions, and explain your solution.

_____

_____

_____

2. With bricks, model $^4/_6 - ^2/_3$. Draw your model, label the fractions, and explain your solution.

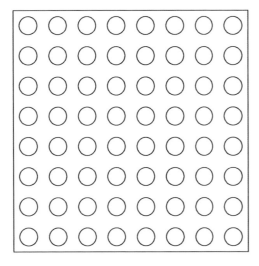 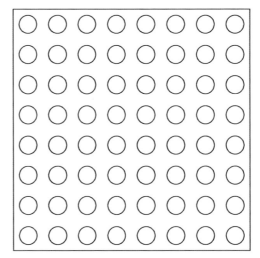

_____
_____
_____

3. What is the difference in the modeling process for addition and subtraction?

_____
_____
_____

MIXED NUMBERS

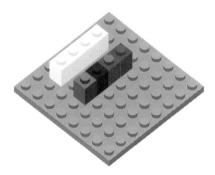

1. This model shows one whole and the parts that make up fourths in that one whole. Build this model. It shows that you can make one whole with $\frac{4}{4}$.

Draw your model and label the fractions.

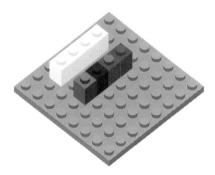

2. With bricks, model 1¼. Draw your model and label the whole and the fourth.

What is this type of fraction called? _____

3. Model 2²⁄₄. Draw your model and label the wholes and the fourths.

With bricks, find another name for this fraction. Draw your solution.

4. With bricks, model 1³⁄₈. Draw and explain your model.

_____

_____

_____

5. With bricks, model $3\frac{4}{10}$. Draw and explain your model.

_____
_____
_____

More problems for practice:

6. With bricks, model $4\frac{2}{3}$. Draw and explain your model.

_____
_____
_____

2. With bricks, model 3⅘. Draw and explain your model.

With bricks, model another way to name this fraction. Draw your model and explain your thinking.

Assessment:

1. Circle the whole number in each fraction below.

  a. $4^2/_3$ **b.** $1^5/_6$ **c.** $7^3/_4$

2. Make a model that shows that you can write one whole as $^3/_3$.

3. Define the term *mixed fraction* or *mixed number*.

_____

_____

_____

4. With bricks, model $3^2/_3$. Draw your model and explain the parts of the fraction.

_____

_____

_____

FRACTION PUZZLE CHALLENGE

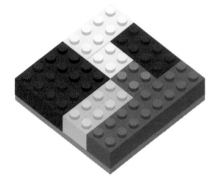

Build this model exactly as you see it, using the same bricks with the same colors.
Use these ten bricks:

Size	Number	Color
1x2	1	light green
2x2	3	dark green, orange, yellow
2x3	1	light green
(or two 1x3 bricks)		
2x4	4	yellow, blue, 2 red
2x6	1	dark green

What is the fractional part of the whole for each color in your model?

Color	Fraction
Yellow	
Red	
Blue	
Dark Green	
Light Green	
Orange	

List all of the combination of colors that are equivalent to ½. (Example: red + dark green = ½)

_____

_____

_____

_____

_____

_____

Challenge:

With bricks, create your own puzzle and questions. Have a partner find the solutions to your puzzle. Draw your puzzle here and list your questions.

_____

_____

_____

Printed in Great Britain
by Amazon